Design
Presentation

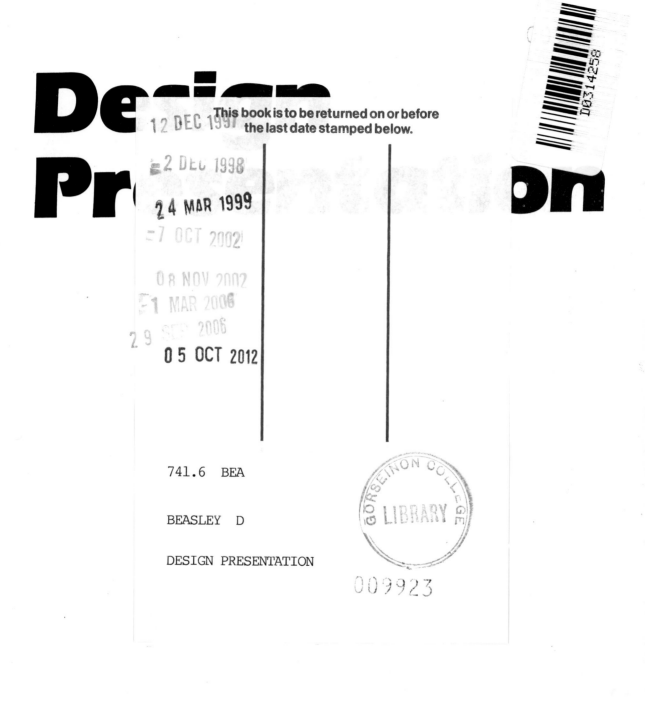

By the same author

Design Illustration
Sketching and shading techniques

Design Presentation

Layout and colouring techniques

David Beasley

Head of Graphic Design
Farnborough College of Technology

HEINEMANN
EDUCATIONAL

Heinemann Educational Books Ltd
Halley Court, Jordan Hill Oxford, OX2 8EJ

OXFORD LONDON EDINBURGH
MADRID ATHENS BOLOGNA PARIS
MELBOURNE SYDNEY AUCKLAND SINGAPORE TOKYO
IBADAN NAIROBI HARARE GABORONE
PORTSMOUTH NH (USA)

ISBN 0 435 75054 2

First published 1984
95 15 14 13 12 11

Printed and Bound in Hong Kong

Preface

Design Presentation has been written to supplement my first book *Design Illustration* which deals with effective ways of drawing and shading pictorial views. This book deals with layout and the application of colour in design drawing.

The book is presented as a basic course and, like its forerunner, recognises the needs of the less artistic student who requires basic rules to guide him or her to communicate effectively in the graphic presentation of design ideas.

The equipment and media used are those commonly found in most educational establishments with perhaps the exception of the airbrush. This is now being used in an increasing number of schools and colleges so its omission would have been inappropriate.

The exercises are designed for A4 sized paper except where stated otherwise and the following basic equipment will be required:

Drawing board (A2 or A3 size)
Drawing board clips or tape
Ruler
Set square
Scissors
Pencils (HB, 2B, and a selection of colours with black and white)
Black ballpoint pen
Water-based markers (colours and grey and black. Ideally ten markers with
  broad tips for shading and at least four markers with fine tips for linework)
White cartridge paper (A4 and A3)
Black sugar paper
Brushwork paper (subdued colours e.g. grey, brown, dull green, dull blue)
Brown wrapping paper

A list of some suitable materials and equipment is given on page 57.

David Beasley

Acknowledgements

The author would like to thank the following for providing photographs:

Page 18:   Letraset UK Ltd., London (dry transfer lettering)
Page 24:   Stallard International Holidays Ltd., London (logo)
Page 33:   Berol Ltd., Kings Lynn (markers)
Page 52:   Morris and Ingram (London) Ltd., Poole (single-action airbrush, Badger 350–M)
       :   The DeVilbiss Company Ltd., Bournemouth (double-action airbrush, Aerograph Sprite)

Contents

Exploring ideas through sketches

Words cannot always adequately describe shape, proportion, form and position. A picture is the clearest way to show these details.

To find out how difficult it can be to work from words alone, ask a partner to describe the shape immediately above 'Fig. 1' on page 40. Then try to sketch it without looking at the picture.

Communicating through a picture is called **graphic communication**. A drawing is a **graphic symbol** which stands for the real object. There are many different types of drawing but this book concentrates on the presentation of **orthographic** and **pictorial drawing**. These are the two main types of drawing likely to be used in the development of a design.

The word 'orthographic' means 'straight drawing' (*ortho* means 'straight' and *graphic* means 'writing' or 'drawing').

The orthographic view in Fig. 1 shows the true shape of the profile of part of a lamp because we are looking at right angles to the surface.

More orthographic views of this part are shown in Fig. 2. From these we can determine the whole form of this part of the lamp.

Fig. 3 gives a complete picture of this part. It is called a pictorial view. The most realistic type of pictorial drawing is the **perspective view**.

The other sketches show more about the construction and assembly of this simple lamp.

Through drawing, ideas can be expressed and explored using sketches as graphic notes. A design can be gradually changed and improved as ideas develop. A designer can develop and present a clear visual image in this way. It is much easier than trying to explain design ideas in words. In design, pictures are usually better than words.

For some aspects of design work orthographic views are perfectly adequate. It might be helpful to draw these on squared paper, as shown in Fig. 4, using the grid as a guide for the horizontal and vertical lines of sketches.

Interest and variety, can be created in the layout of sketches on a page by contrasting orthographic and pictorial views. Pictorial views should be included. They provide a realistic view of the design for people who are not used to orthographic views.

Exercise 1
Draw freehand with an HB pencil, orthographic and pictorial views of one of the following:
A torch; camera; bicycle lamp; bicycle bell; table lamp; radio; stapler; paper punch; any other suitable object of similar difficulty.
Follow the style of the linework on the opposite page. As shown there, do not be too careful about finishing exactly at a corner.

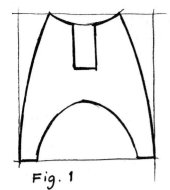

Fig. 1

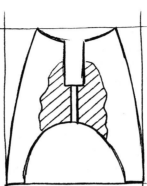

Orthographic view
sectioned to show
hole for cable.

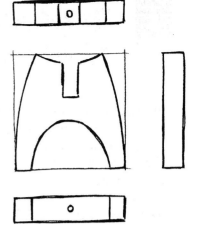

Fig. 2

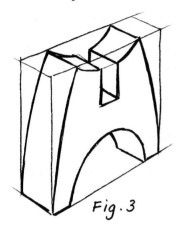

Fig. 3

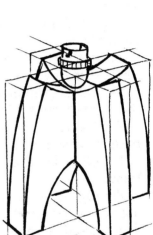

Pictorial view
showing parts
assembled.

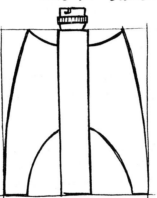

Orthographic view
of assembled parts.

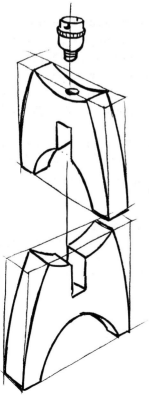

'Exploded'
pictorial
view shows
how parts
fit
together.

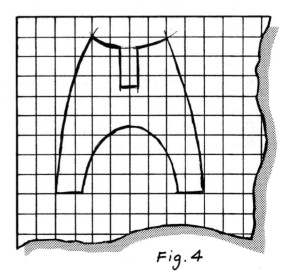

Fig. 4

2 Drawing in boxes

Graphic notes do not have to be perfect illustrations since they are only for ideas which are jotted down very quickly. However, your sketches need to be recognisable. A page of scribble which only you can understand is of little use in showing the way that your design was developed and it is not very interesting to look at.

Your sketching can be improved by imagining that the object that you are drawing has been packed into a transparent 'box' or 'crate', and that it is such a tight fit that the faces of the object are touching the sides of the crate. This crate can be lightly drawn as a guide for drawing either an orthographic view or a pictorial view.

When sketching a crate for a pictorial view it can either be sketched as in Fig. 1 with parallel edges, like an isometric view, or as in Fig. 2 with tapering edges giving a perspective view. The amount of tapering is not important in sketching. Vanishing points do not have to be constructed or even marked.

Opposite are sketched designs for the body of a simple car. It will be cut out of a block of wood using only straight saw cuts. Each view has been drawn within a crate to show the block of wood before it is sawn. The cars are drawn with thicker lines so that they stand out and so the crates do not have to be erased.

As you can see the sketches have not been drawn with precision. Note, for instance, that the edges of a crate do not meet exactly but extend beyond the corners. This helps to show that these sketches are only possible solutions to the problem and that the design is not yet complete. A neat crate would give the impression that the design was finished.

Drawing crates like this is called 'crating'. Crating is a useful technique which is widely used by artists and designers. It helps them draw complicated shapes and to work out proportions and positions. Crates have been used to help in drawing the chair in Fig. 3. As a result the positions of the legs are easier to plot and the shape of the seat is easier to draw.

Exercise 2
Design some bodies of lorries or other commercial vehicles which can be made from blocks of wood using only straight saw cuts.

Use crates to help you sketch at least eight different designs.

Draw a selection of orthographic and pictorial views on the same sheet.

Label the type of vehicles that you have designed.

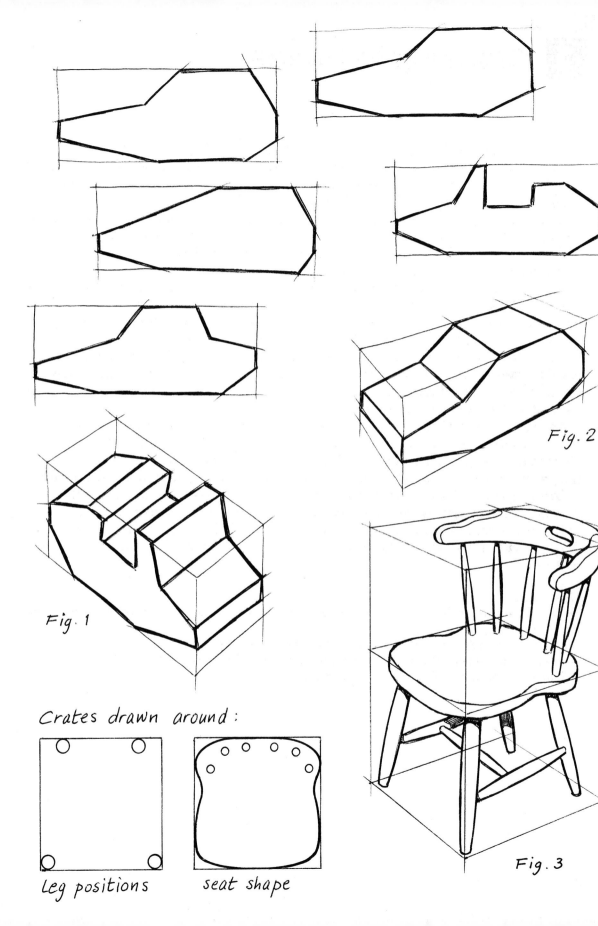

Fig. 2

Fig. 1

Crates drawn around:

Leg positions

seat shape

Fig. 3

3 Through thick and thin

The sketches opposite are designs for buildings suitable for use with a model railway. The buildings are to be made from blocks of wood. They can be covered with pieces of coloured paper or painted to make them more realistic.

All the lines of the building in Fig. 1 have been made thicker to make it stand out from the surrounding crate. This same building is shown in Fig. 2 but some of the lines have been made thicker than others.

Thick and thin lines produce a type of shadow effect which makes a drawing clearer. They introduce the important element of contrast, which gives visual interest. Technical artists and illustrators commonly use this line technique. Examples can be found in a wide variety of line illustrations including 'exploded' parts drawings and cutaway views of cars, motor-cycles and other mechanical devices.

You cannot draw thick and thin lines exactly where you like. The rules for deciding whether a line should be thick or thin on an illustration are as follows:

1   A line where two surfaces meet and where *both* surfaces can be seen is a *thin* line.
2   A line where two surfaces meet and where only *one* surface can be seen is a *thick* line.

For example, in Fig. 2 the line representing the front edge of the building is indicated by Arrow A. It is a thin line because both the front and the side surfaces which meet at this edge can be seen. A thick line has been used on the edge of the roof indicated by Arrow B. This is because the side of the building which meets this edge is hidden.

These rules can be used for curved lines as well as straight lines, as shown in the arch in Fig. 3.

The lower illustrations show part of a large oil pump. Fig. 6 shows the illustration without any difference in line thickness. In Fig. 7 the thick and thin technique has been applied in part of the drawing, so that your attention is drawn to some parts only. In Fig. 8 thick and thin lines have been applied to the whole illustration.

Exercise 3
1   Draw the buildings shown in Figs. 4 and 5 about twice the printed size. Apply the thick and thin line technique to your drawings.

2   Sketch at least six of your own designs for similar block buildings. Apply the thick and thin line technique to your three best designs.

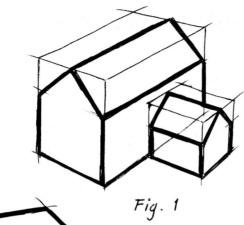

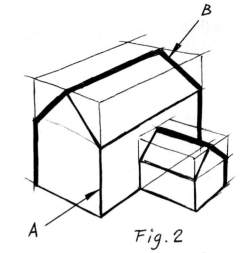

Fig. 1

B

A

Fig. 2

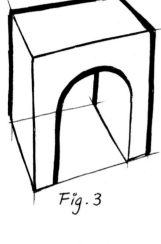

Fig. 3

Fig. 5

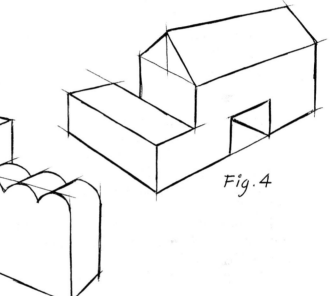

Fig. 4

Fig. 6

Fig. 7

Fig. 8

4 Design sheet layout

The planning for any design assignment is likely to consist of sketches and written notes on several sheets. These sheets should look as if they belong together. This can be achieved in the following ways:

1 Keep all the sheets the same size.
2 Keep the same basic layout for all your sheets. For example if a border is used on one sheet as in Fig. 1, then the other sheets should have the same border. Keep all the sheets the same, whether you prefer to use a border or not.
3 The design of the title block can be imaginative in the use of lettering and colour. It should also be the same on each sheet. Some possibilities for title blocks are given in Fig. 2.
4 The sheets should be numbered in order and each sheet should bear the title of the assignment, your name and the date.

The first sheet of a design assignment usually states the problem and includes notes which provide information about the problem. Questions such as 'What is it for?', 'Who will use it?', 'Where will it be used?' and 'Of what could it be made', need to be answered. This will help you to make some decisions and so narrow down the range of possible solutions.

You need, therefore, to decide on a layout for sheets which contain notes. Bear in mind that when notes run right across the page, as in Fig. 3, they can be difficult to follow from one line to the next. A different layout, in which the notes are easier to follow is shown in Fig. 4. The sheet is divided into more visually interesting proportions. In this arrangement the notes have been restricted to about one-third of the page with sketches providing a contrast with the notes. If more space for notes is required they may be continued on the next sheet keeping to the same layout.

Exercise 4
Sketch six possible layouts for design sheets. Use colour for some headings or for the backgrounds to the headings. Select the design you like best and give reasons for your choice.

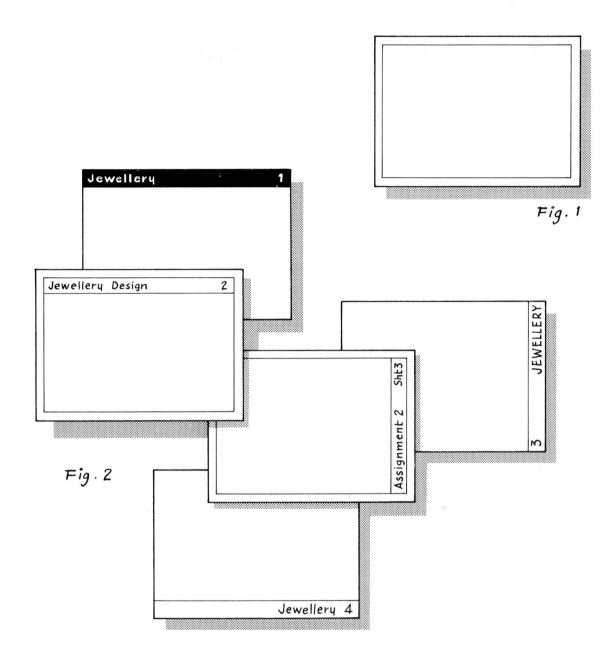

Fig. 1

Fig. 2

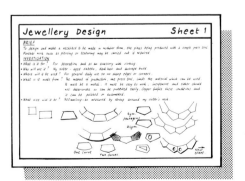

Fig. 3

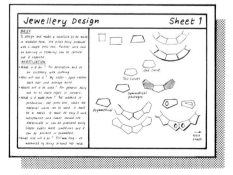

Fig. 4

5 Lettering

The notes and drawings on design sheets are a record of the stages in the development of a solution to a problem. Both are important but handwritten notes are often difficult to read. They can spoil a good presentation.

When making notes use neat, simple letters, avoiding loops and fancy decorative styles.

Draw light guide lines to keep lines of lettering straight and to control the height of the letters.

Ensure that adequate space is left between pairs of guide lines to fit in loops and strokes of letters like 'g' and 'p'.

An example of simple hand-lettered characters drawn within guide lines is shown in Fig. 1.

Another way to provide guide lines for letters is to slip a page ruled with black lines under your design sheet. This only works if the lines can be seen through the paper.

Exercise 5A

1   Draw pencil guide lines 4 mm apart and letter the characters shown in Fig. 1 using:
    (a) an HB pencil; (b) a ballpoint pen; (c) a marker with a fine tip.

2   Copy Fig. 2 using 5 mm high letters for the heading and 4 mm high letters for the wording.

It is difficult to keep letters exactly upright all the time. Any which lean away from the vertical, even slightly, will attract the eye. To avoid this problem, many people slope all their letters. Then, if one letter slopes at a slightly different angle to the rest, it is not so noticeable as it would have been amongst upright letters. Fig. 3 is an example of characters produced in a sloping style.

Contrast is extremely useful in graphic work. It creates variety and interest. This applies as much to lettering as it does to layout and illustrations. In lettering, contrast can be achieved by using capital letters. (upper case) for headings and small letters (lower case) for notes and sub-headings (as in Figs. 4 and 5) and also by using different colours for each.

Exercise 5B

1   Repeat Exercise 5A question 1, using the sloping style of letters shown in Fig. 3.

2   Use sloping characters to copy Fig. 2. Letter the headings in 5 mm high characters with a red marker and letter the rest in 4 mm high characters in green.

3   Set out and line in neatly on A3 paper, the design sheet which you selected as your best layout in answer to Exercise 4.
    Complete the sheet with neat lettered headings.

UPPER CASE :

ABCDEFGHIJKLMNOPQRSTUVWXYZ

lower case :

abcdefghijklmnopqrstuvwxyz

NUMERALS :

1234567890

Fig. 1

DESIGN ASSIGNMENT

Design and make a container
to stand on a desk and which
will hold paper clips, rubber
bands, pencils and an eraser.

Fig. 2

4mm 4mm 4mm 4mm 4mm 4mm

UPPER CASE :

ABCDEFGHIJKLMNOPQRSTUVWXYZ

lower case :

abcdefghijklmnopqrstuvwxyz

NUMERALS

1234567890

Fig. 3

BRIEF
Design and make a container
will hold paper clips, rubber
INVESTIGATION
Who will use it ? All the far
Where ? Mai

Fig. 4

DESK CONTAINER DESIGN
10 Aug. 1983
G. Lovegrove

Fig. 5

Sheet 2

6 Shade and form

Pencil shading can be used to improve the impact of a drawing. If this shading is to look realistic, the effect of light must be taken into account

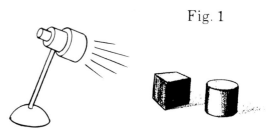

Fig. 1

When light falls on an object, surfaces reflect different amounts of light depending on their position in relation to the light source. In Fig. 1 the solid forms are illuminated by the lamp. You can see that the side which faces towards the light looks lighter than that which faces away from the light. With the cylinder, the part directly facing the light source is the lightest.

To make shading easier the form of most man-made articles can be simplified into the standard solid forms shown in Fig. 2, or into forms similar to them. For example, the drawing of the cine-camera in Fig. 3 can be simplified into the solid forms shown in the 'exploded' view.

To shade a drawing, it must be imagined that light falls from a direction so that the form of the object is shown at its best. In Fig. 3 light falls from the top left-hand corner and the shading has been added to suit this.

When shading, use a soft lead pencil to give a wide range of tones from light grey to dense black. It will be difficult to obtain dark enough shading with any grade of pencil harder than HB. The most suitable grades are 2B, B and HB.

The area to be shaded can be covered quickly and evenly if the pencil is held as in Fig. 4 so that it is nearly horizontal. In this position more lead is in contact with the paper whereas if the pencil is held upright in the normal way the covering would be more streaky.

This shading is called TONAL SHADING because one colour is used and the form of an object is shown through the tonal differences.

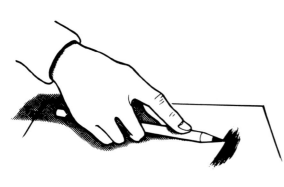

Fig. 4

Exercise 6

1 Draw, with light lines, the six squares shown in Fig. 5. Each side measures 30 mm. Shade each square so that the join between two squares is only shown by the difference in the shading.

2 Draw the view of the cine-camera in Fig. 3 about twice the printed size. Shade your drawing imagining that the light falls from the top right-hand corner.

3 Draw the objects shown in Fig. 6 about twice the printed size. Decide from where light should fall for each object and use a soft pencil to shade your drawings realistically.

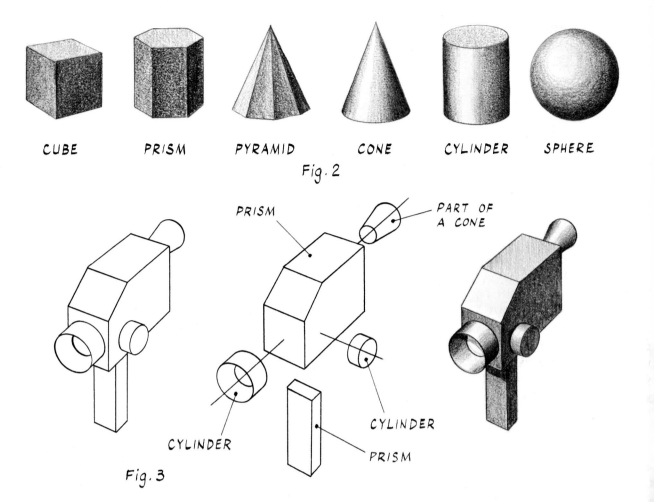

CUBE   PRISM   PYRAMID   CONE   CYLINDER   SPHERE

Fig. 2

PRISM

PART OF A CONE

CYLINDER

CYLINDER

PRISM

Fig. 3

Fig. 5

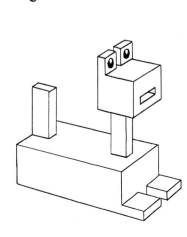

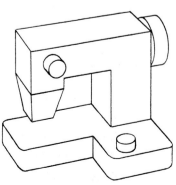

Fig. 6

7 Light and form

Dark paper is particularly effective when designing something that will be made from a shiny or polished material such as perspex or silver. The sketches opposite are designs for small trinket boxes to be made out of metal and they were drawn on black sugar paper. With this paper it is best to work on the side with the rougher, more heavily textured surface since a greater range of shaded effects can be produced.

On light paper the form of an object is shown by shading the shadowed areas. On dark paper reflections and highlights are emphasized. Apart from this, toning with a white pencil is similar to shading with a lead pencil. The position of the light source has to be imagined and the toning applied according to the effect that this light would have on the object.

With a curved surface however, as well as the bright highlight, the edges appear lighter. This is because the surface, curving away from the eye, catches light reflected from surrounding surfaces. When shading, particularly on coloured backgrounds, this effect can be used to emphasize a curved surface. White pencilled shading has been used to show this reflected light in Fig. 1.

A version of the thick and thin line technique has been used for the additional linework in Figs. 1 and 2 to give more realistic illustrations.

The stages used for the thick and thin line technique on dark paper are as follows. They are shown in the sequence in Fig. 3:

Fig. 3A   A shaded sketch has been produced with a white pencil. The lower reflections show that the box is standing on a surface.

Fig. 3B   Those edges where only one surface can be seen have been lined in with black coloured pencil. The point of the pencil should be sharp to give a crisp finished edge to the white shading which always tends to be uneven at the edges.

Fig. 3C   Lines which normally remain thin (those edges where two surfaces can be seen) should be made as bright as possible. Use a sharp white pencil. The brightest highlights can then be made even whiter, if required, with white paint or ink. To do this, water colour, poster colour, white ink or any other suitable medium can be used. It should be applied with a fine brush or a ruling pen. Paint, thinned with water, will flow in a ruling pen (Fig. 4) which is particularly useful when straight lines are required.

Fig. 4

Notes which accompany sketches can also be written with a white pencil or ink. If white ink is not available, thinned-down paint can be used with a nib in a holder.

Exercise 7

1   Use a white pencil to copy on black paper the drawing of the box in Fig. 3 about three times the printed size. Complete your illustration by following the shading sequence explained in this chapter.

2   Use a white pencil to sketch on black paper six of your own designs for a small box. Follow the shading sequence to produce better illustrations of what you consider are your two best designs.

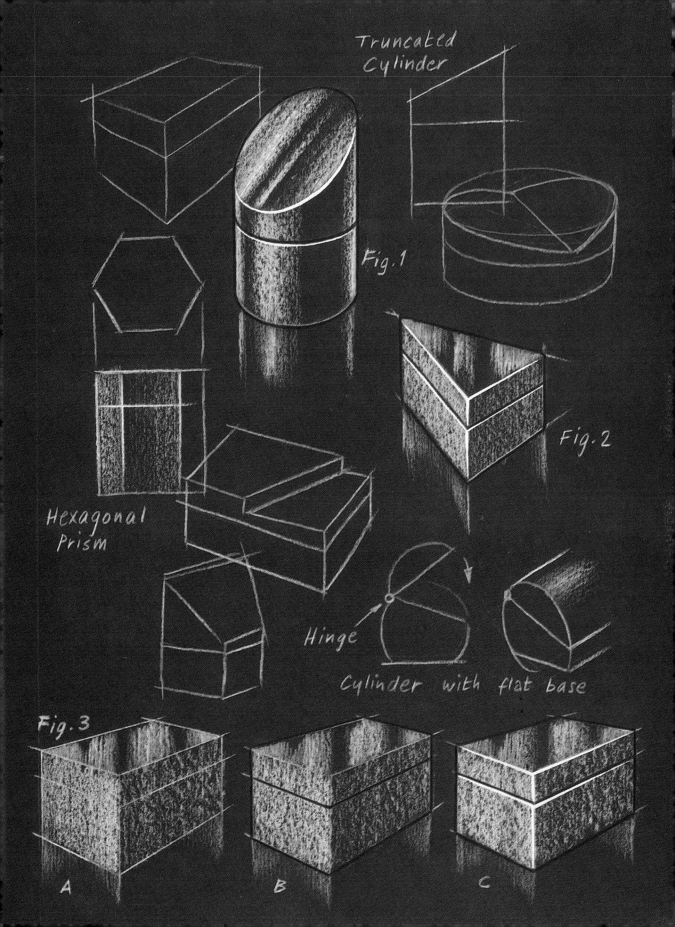

Truncated Cylinder

Fig.1

Hexagonal Prism

Fig.2

Hinge

Cylinder with flat base

Fig.3

A   B   C

8 Line shading

Another method of shading is shown opposite where lines have been used to imitate the tonal differences produced when light falls on an object. The lines can vary in thickness and in spacing. When they follow the form of the object the shading is known as **form shading**.

Form shading on objects which have straight sides follows in the same direction as one of the edges of the surface being shaded (Figs. 1 and 2).

Form shading on curved surfaces also follows one edge but it is quicker and easier to shade if a straight edge can be followed, as in the examples of the cone and cylinder (Figs. 3 and 4). Drawing a series of ellipses to indicate form as in Fig. 5 is difficult and takes more time.

Another type of line shading is **hatching**. Lines are drawn which do not follow the direction of any of the edges of an object. Examples of this are shown in Fig. 6 where surfaces have been 'hatched' and in Fig. 7 where **cross-hatching** has been used. 'Cross-hatched' means hatched in two directions.

Part of a 'cutaway and exploded' view in which line shading has been used is shown in Fig. 8. What other illustrative technique has been used here?

Exercise 8

1 Sketch your own version of each of the condiment containers shown in Figs. 1–6 opposite. Apply form shading and the thick and thin lines technique to your sketches.

2 Make two sketches of the building shown in Fig. 1 on page 6. 'Hatch' one of these sketches and 'cross-hatch' the other, thinking about the effect of light.

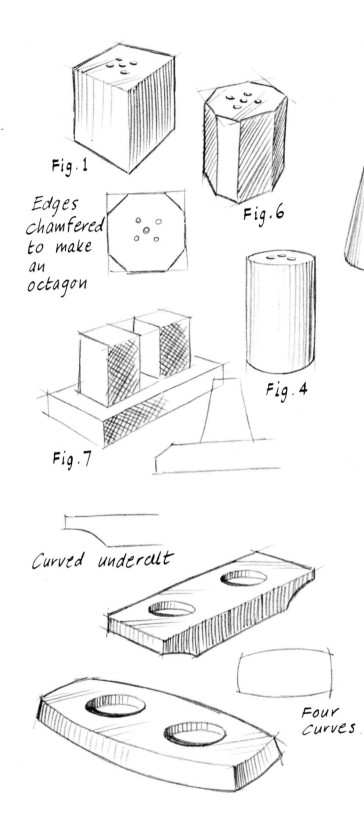

Fig. 1

Edges
chamfered
to make
an
octagon

Fig. 6

Fig. 4

Fig. 7

Curved undercut

Four Curves.

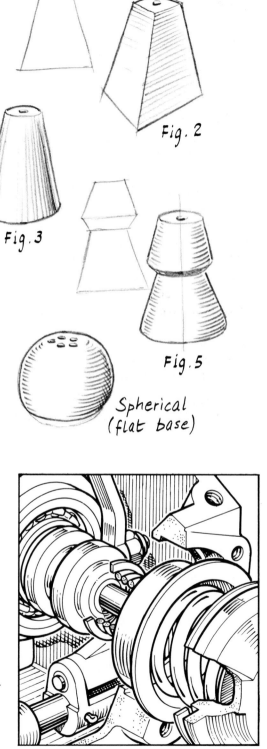

Fig. 2

Fig. 3

Fig. 5

Spherical
(flat base)

Fig. 8

9 Further lettering

Thick and thin strokes are used in lettering because they look better than strokes of a uniform thickness. You can do this by using a pen or pencil which has a flat tip. You can use pens or markers with broad nibs or tips, or a lead pencil which has been sharpened with a blade or glasspaper to a chisel tip. This is shown in Fig. 1.

Nibs with broad tips can be bought to fit ordinary nib-holders, fountain pens and some types of technical pens.

A broad tipped pen or pencil with a chisel tip must always be held at the same angle to the paper then the thick and thin strokes will follow automatically. The pen must be held naturally and should not be twisted or turned in an artificial manner.

Exercise 9
Sharpen the lead of an HB pencil to a chisel tip and use it for the following:
(a) A 'doodle' is shown in Fig. 2. Get used to using the chisel-edged pencil by producing your own doodle.
(b) Copy the characters shown in Fig. 3. Use guide lines drawn 5 mm apart.
(c) Letter the following heading and notes deciding on the height of the letters for yourself:

DESIGN BRIEF
Design and make a wooden toy which moves because it uses a spring.

There are two methods of producing lettering which can give a professional finish. Both methods take longer than lettering by hand and are therefore unlikely to be used for notes on design sheets. However, they would be useful for the main titles on these sheets; for lettering on a cover or folder; or for display work.

Stencils

A lettering stencil is a guide in which letters have been pierced out of a plastic strip. Two examples are shown in Fig. 4. There are stencils which are made for many different styles and size of letters. Some are suitable for a pencil and some for a pen. Usually a technical pen or a special stencil pen has to be used although a ballpoint pen can be used with some stencils. Fig. 5 shows a lettering stencil and pen in use and Fig. 6 is an example of stencilled lettering.

Dry-transfer lettering

This method uses sheets of letters which can be transferred individually to the work by rubbing with a pen or pencil over each letter after it has been placed in the required position. Fig. 7 shows two stages in transferring a letter.

There is an enormous range of styles and sizes of lettering. Fig. 8 gives a few examples. The title block in Fig. 9 was produced with dry-transfer lettering.

UPPER CASE

ABCDEFGHIJKLMNOPQRSTUVWXYZ

lower case

abcdefghijklmnopqrstuvwxyz

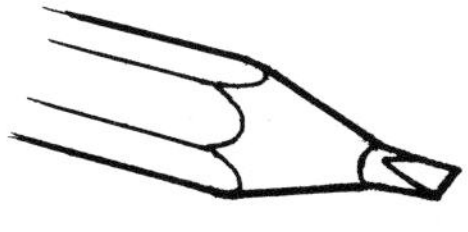

Fig. 1

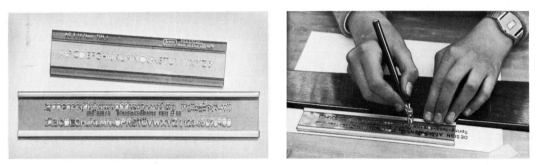

Fig. 2

NUMERALS

1234567890

Fig. 3

Fig. 4   Fig. 5

ABCDEFGHIJKLMNOPQRSTUVWXYZ
abcdefghijklmnopqrstuvwxyz
1234567890

Fig. 6

AAAAAAAAAAAAAAA

Fig. 8

Fig. 7   Fig. 9

ENAMELLED BROOCH
4 June 1983
Heather Davies   Sheet 2

10 Pictures on a page

Figs. 1 and 2 show two arrangements of the same sketches. Fig. 1 is a rather formal arrangement in which the sketches have been drawn in neat rows. Fig. 2 is a more haphazard layout in which the sketches are not evenly spaced and some overlapping occurs.

Both of these arrangements are acceptable but if you want your design sheets to be interesting to look at and to attract the eye then you should try to sketch freely and not be overconcerned about spacing sketches evenly. Allow them to touch and overlap as in Fig. 2.

There is a good reason for this approach. From a purely visual point of view, the background is as important as what is actually on the background.

Imagine that the sketches in Figs. 1 and 2 have been cut from the two sheets and that these sheets have then been placed on dark backgrounds. In Fig. 4, which is the cut-out version of Fig. 2, interest is created by the contrast in pattern between single and overlapping cut-outs, by the unusual shapes produced and by the variation in distance between the cut-outs. Fig. 3 is the cut-out version of Fig. 1. There are no surprising features which compel the eye to explore the page. Once again it can be seen that contrast, in this case between groups of shapes and between the spaces that result, makes graphic work more interesting.

Whenever you wish to create an interesting display, you should always try to introduce variation and contrast, as for example when you are considering the position of a sketch on a page; hanging pictures on a wall; or arranging notices on a notice board.

Exercise 10

Cut out at least six pictures from magazines which show alternative designs for the same product. These could be television sets, chairs, table lamps, cups, glasses, electric toasters or anything you choose.

Arrange the pictures in a formal way on A3 paper, taping them in position. Trace the pictures on to tracing paper, omitting the finer details. If tracing paper is not available, tape the sheet of pictures on to a window and use the light to help you trace the main forms onto a sheet of cartridge paper.

Repeat the exercise but this time make an informal arrangement with the same pictures.

Look at the two arrangements and decide which you prefer, writing your reasons down on the appropriate sheet.

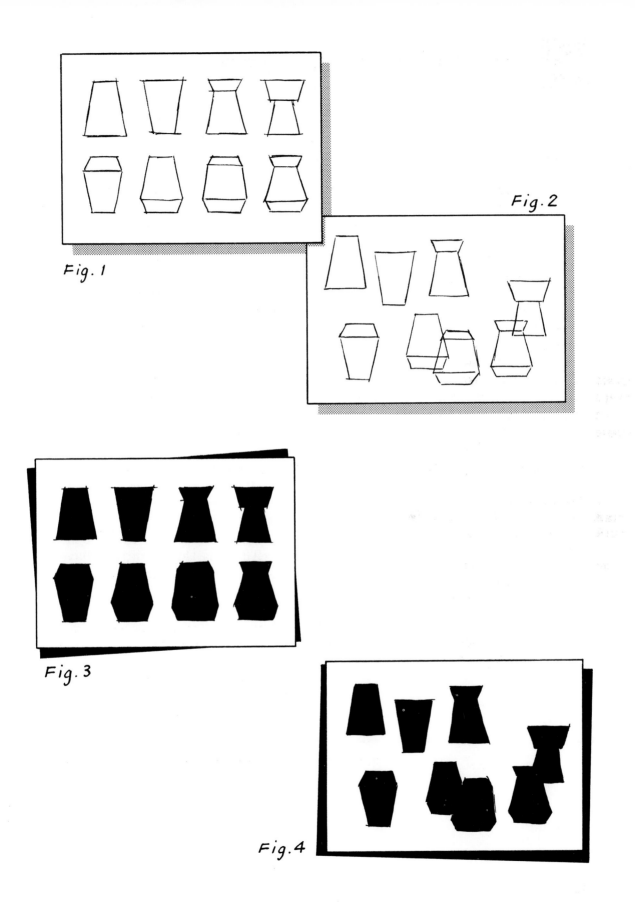

Fig. 1

Fig. 2

Fig. 3

Fig. 4

■ Using cut-out pictures

Magazines and catalogues can be very useful in design work for sparking off ideas, for reviewing commercially available products and for preparing illustrations.

'Getting started' is notoriously difficult in design work. Considerable time may be wasted in trying to think up ideas or in deciding on a suitable theme. A stock of old magazines costs nothing and can be of great benefit as reference material to help inspiration.

The problems which arise in design work have usually been solved many times before, perhaps in a variety of ways, and the resulting products may be advertised or featured in magazines. Therefore, in the development of a design, the analysis of the problem could also involve an investigation into the solutions of other people. If pictures of these solutions are available they should be included in the design development. It is common sense to study the work of other people. To do so indicates an approach which is thorough and honest, provided the end product is a result of your own development and not mere copying.

The page shown in Fig. 1 is part of the design development for a wall lamp. Pictures of lamps have been cut out and arranged on a page to show differences in form and construction. There are also brief notes about each. The notes are as important as the pictures since they explain how and why you consider that the products succeed or fail as solutions to the problem.

You can make collections of cut-out pictures for use as reference material. The two books shown in Fig. 2 are collections of hands and of people. They are useful when a particular pose is required for a drawing. Picture collections on one particular theme or of a general nature can be compiled. Similar books of reference pictures are available commercially but they are usually very expensive.

Figures 3, 4, and 5 are combinations of drawings and cut-out pictures where the pictures are used to give added realism to proposed designs. Cut-out pictures have been used as backgrounds for the drawings of the necklace in Fig. 3 and the coffee table in Fig. 4. They give a touch of realism to the photographic display stands in Fig. 5.

Exercise 11
Collect old colour supplements, magazines and catalogues.
Make a collection of cuttings which will be useful in your work.

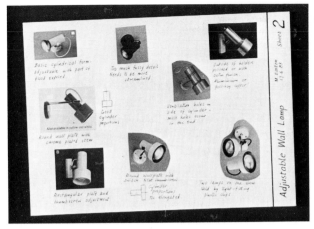

Fig. 1

Fig. 2

Fig.3

Fig.4

Fig.5

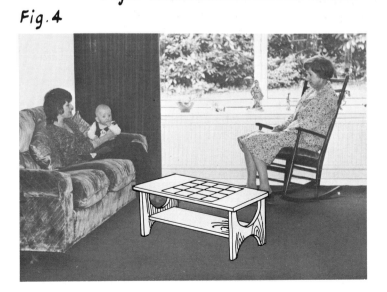

12 Shadows

Where there is light there will also be shadow. The inclusion of a shadow cast by an object can make a sketch more realistic.

The views in Fig. 1 are plans of buildings with their shadows falling on the ground. Fig. 2 shows the same buildings but with the light source in a different position. The shapes of the shadows for A and B have not altered but it is now more difficult to interpret the form of the other buildings. Can you describe the form of each building from its shadow? The answers are at the foot of page 35.

When illustrating, the imaginary position of the light source can be anywhere — light can fall in any convenient direction — but as Figs. 1 and 2 show, with flat-sided objects it is best if the light falls towards one corner, rather than directly onto one face.

In Fig. 3 the imaginary light falls towards the top left-hand corner of each of the thin decorative pieces. The diagrams show that edges which face away from the light source will cast shadows.

It is best to imagine that light falls towards the **top** corner of a two-dimensional view as in these examples since shadows are normally seen in this way in our environment. Light usually falls from above either from the sun or from artificial light. Fig. 4 shows two pictures hanging on a wall, one lit from above and the other from below. Which shadow appears most realistic?

The colour of a shadow is always a darker shade of the colour of the surface on which it falls, so for instance a shadow falling on a blue surface will be a darker blue. In the examples opposite the shadows are falling on white paper so the shadows are 'dark white' which of course is grey. On white paper shadows can be added with a soft lead pencil or a grey marker.

Designs for decorative pieces which include curved edges are shown in Fig. 5. The way to find the exact points where the shadows meet the curved edges in Fig. 5A can be seen in Fig. 5B. The lines follow the direction of the light and are tangents to the curves. You only need to imagine these lines when you add shadows to sketches to ensure that the shapes of the shadows are approximately correct.

Other examples of the use of cast shadows are in Fig. 6 where the letters look three-dimensional, and in Fig. 7 where shadows indicate the alcoves and doors of the cupboard unit.

Exercise 12

1 Sketch the pieces shown in Figs. 3 and 5 assuming that light falls from the top RIGHT. Make your sketches about twice the printed size and add some shadows with a lead pencil and some with a marker.

2 Sketch six pierced shapes for a pendant of your own design on one of the following themes: flight; circles and triangles; water; military decorations; sport.
   Decide for yourself the position of a suitable light source and add shadows accordingly. Add a note to each sketch explaining how your design fits the theme.

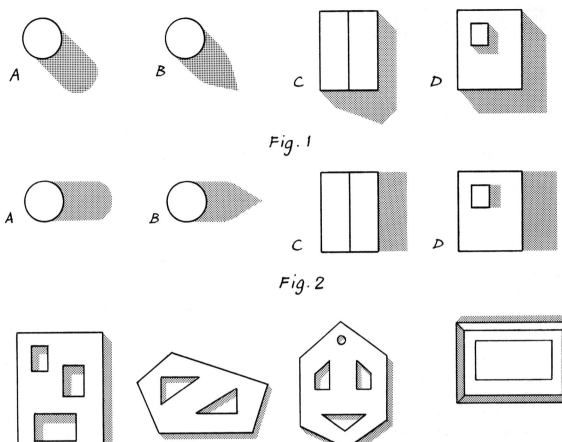

Fig. 1

Fig. 2

Fig. 3

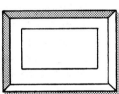

Fig. 4

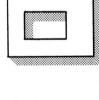

Fig. 5

Fig. 6

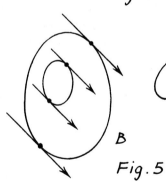

Fig. 7

13 Coloured surrounds

One of the most obvious and effective ways to attract attention is through the use of colour. Perhaps the easiest way to use colour so that a sketch stands out is to colour the surrounding area.

The sketches opposite show designs for a salad fork. It is to be made from pieces of veneer, which have been glued and clamped between shaped blocks whilst the glue is setting to produce the required form. Areas around some sketches have been coloured and notes added for explanation. Notice that the colour is taken right up to the outline so that the sketch can be clearly seen.

The green area around the orthographic view has been shaded with a coloured pencil and becomes progressively fainter away from the outline. This has been achieved by easing the pressure on the pencil to allow the colour to fade into the white of the paper. This effect is called a **vignette**.

The areas around the pictorial views have been coloured with markers. It is impossible to produce a vignette with a marker since neither heavy nor light pressure changes the colour. When markers are used it is best to have an irregular edge to the coloured area so as not to take attention away from the sketch within. Here are some examples of surround shading:

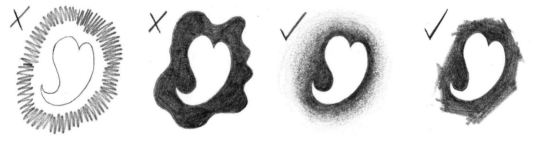

INCORRECT	INCORRECT	CORRECT	CORRECT
The eye is drawn to the peculiar surround.	The surround has taken a dominant shape of its own.	The gradual increase in colour emphasises the shape.	An irregular outline does not detract from the shape inside.

When shading surrounding areas, choose colours which are subdued such as greys, browns, dull greens, and dull blues. Bright colours give a gaudy effect and can be distracting, particularly when several different colours are used.

Exercise 13
Sketch six designs for a spoon or spatula to make a pair with one of the salad forks. Draw orthographic views and a pictorial view of the one you consider to be the best design.

Use a coloured pencil to colour around one sketch, and a marker to colour around another. Use either of these two methods for the pictorial view.

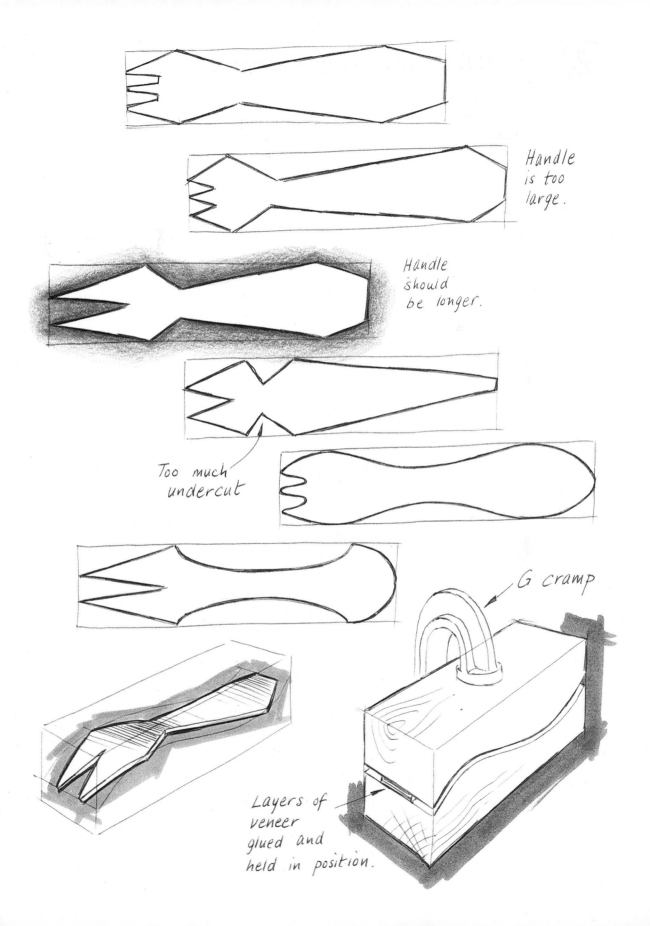

Handle is too large.

Handle should be longer.

Too much undercut

G cramp

Layers of veneer glued and held in position.

14 Colouring flat surfaces

On the opposite page are sketches for name plates which can be made from a variety of sheet materials. Coloured pencils and markers have been used to colour the sketches.

In Fig. 1, colour has been applied evenly but, apart from indicating the colour of the name plate, there are no further clues as to the material or the finish which will be used.

In most plastics, metals, or painted surfaces reflections can be seen. Some indication of these helps to relieve a plain surface. Reflections in a very shiny surface show definite images of things nearby. It would be confusing to include these in a sketch and so it is best, as in Fig. 2, to use reflections which have no clearly recognisable shape. Reflections drawn to show a shiny surface should run roughly diagonally to contrast with horizontal and vertical outlines.

The effect in Fig. 3 was produced with a coloured pencil because the tonal value of the colour can be easily varied. The colour has been blended from light to dark in strips to indicate reflections on the surface.

The following are more formal techniques to indicate certain materials.

Fig. 4   To show wood, dark brown lines are used to indicate the grain over a lighter brown background.

Fig. 5   To show a shiny metallic surface such as silver or chrome plating, light blue strips are used, some of which are drawn over grey lines.

Fig. 6   To show gold or brass, a similar technique is used with deep yellow and dark brown.

Material which has rounded edges needs different treatment. Fig. 7 shows how light falling on a curved edge which is facing towards a light source will reflect light to the eye. An edge facing away from the light source will reflect light away from the eye.

Imagine that the edges of the plate in Fig. 8 are rounded and that light falls from the top left. Strips have been left uncoloured to indicate reflections and, to indicate the shadowed areas, strips have been added which are a darker shade of the surface colour.

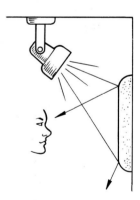

Fig. 7

Exercise 14

Using your own name or initials and a similar style of letters to those shown opposite, sketch six designs for a name plate.

Colour your design sketches using the techniques described above.

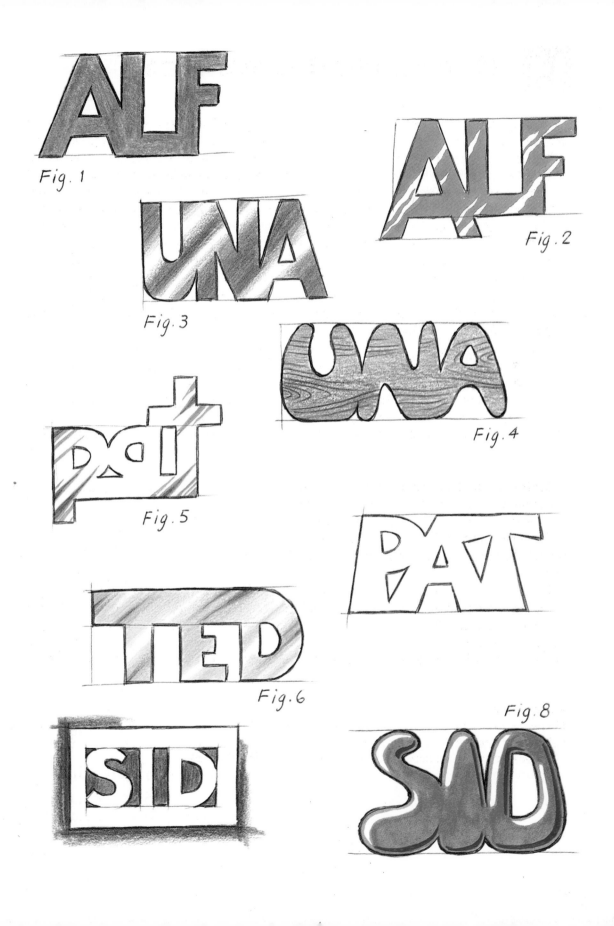

Fig. 1

Fig. 2

Fig. 3

Fig. 4

Fig. 5

Fig. 6

Fig. 8

15 Examples of two-dimensional presentation

The techniques which have been described in the preceding pages have been used to improve the presentation of the page of design sketches opposite.

These show some possible solutions to a design problem in which a piece of acrylic sheet is to be shaped so that it is suitable for a key fob, a pendant, or a door plaque. The theme for the shapes was 'Creatures' and to keep the designs simple they had to be drawn inside common geometrical shapes. Can you say which five presentation techniques have been used on the opposite page? The answers are listed below.

Exercise 15
Produce a sheet of sketches showing your own solutions to the above problem. Use the same geometric shapes if you wish but draw different creatures to those shown. Improve the presentation of your page and draw attention to what you consider are your best designs by applying any of the colouring and shadow techniques.

Answers

1   The creatures have been drawn with thicker lines to contrast with the thin lines of the geometric shapes or 'crates'. The surrounding shapes remain to show the development process.

2   The areas around the dove and the modified elephant's trunk have been coloured.

3   The shiny nature of acrylic sheet has been indicated by the reflections on the anteater and the owl.

4   The reflections and the shadowed areas of the snake show that the material has curved edges.

5   The grey shadows of the elephant and the snake help to show the thickness of the material to be used.

29

Cats (Ovals)

Dove (circle)

Elephant (square)

Weakness in trunk - perhaps better like this

Anteater (semi-circle)

Owl (Oval)

Snake (rectangle)

Section through snake body

Octopus (circle segment)

16 Colouring with pencils

Coloured pencils have been popular for many years because they provide an effective and inexpensive way of applying colour quickly and easily without any mess.

By varying the pressure on a pencil a wide range of tonal values from a light tint to a dense covering can be obtained. This enables surfaces to be shaded realistically to suit the effect of light, as described in Chapter 6. Fig. 1 shows three tonal values achieved with one coloured pencil to show the form of the block.

Although coloured pencils are not graded like lead pencils, some manufacturers' pencils are softer than others. To obtain a dense covering of colour, pencils with softer points should be used. Try out various makes before you buy to see which deposit most colour.

When shading with coloured pencils hold them, as with lead pencils, in the near-horizontal position, so that more of the point is in contact with the paper. Do *not* be afraid to press hard if you require dense colours. Many people spoil their presentation because they fail to obtain the necessary contrast between tones.

If you have two variations of the *same* colour (one light and one dark) in your pencil collection, you can use them to produce the effect in Fig. 2. Surfaces facing upwards remain white, surfaces which face the light are shaded with the lighter colour and those which face away from the light are shaded with the darker colour.

The part of a curved surface nearest to the light source, the **highlight**, reflects most light. This is shown in Fig. 3 where the shading fades out so that the white of the paper is used for the highlight.

Exercise 16

1   Draw one of the pictorial views opposite and use only one coloured pencil to show the effect of light on the object.

2   Draw a different pictorial view and use two coloured pencils — light and dark variations of the same colour — to show the effect of light. Leave surfaces facing upwards white.

3   Sketch three of your own designs for pencil holders. Use coloured pencils to shade the one which you consider the best.

Fig. 1

Fig. 3

Fig. 2

Eraser

17 Colouring with markers

When using markers for design drawing you should use those which have a water-soluble base. The colouring from these will not pass through thinner paper as spirit-based markers often do.

Markers are available for a wide range of drawing and colouring purposes and consequently their tips vary in shape and size. Fig. 1 shows examples of markers which are suitable for linework, shading and lettering.

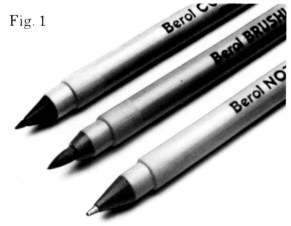

Fig. 1

Changing the pressure on a marker will not vary the colour produced. If only one marker is used and the effect of light on the object is to be shown, then form or line shading must be adopted. An example of this is shown in Fig. 2.

Two markers were used to colour Fig. 3, one a darker green than the other. In Fig. 4, although only one green marker was used, the darker green was obtained by first shading the surface with a grey marker and then applying green over the grey.

Form shading has been used on the cylinder in Fig. 5. This has been taken a stage further in Fig. 6 where a series of bars has been drawn. They get narrower and are spaced further apart the nearer they get to the highlight. This technique is called **bar shading**. On the bar shading in Fig. 7, a darker marker has also been used to emphasize the shadowed areas.

The remaining sketches on the opposite page are designs for painted wooden animals, each of which contains a spring to produce some form of movement.

Exercise 17

1 Copy, about twice the printed size, two of the design sketches opposite which have not been coloured. Shade them with markers using the methods described above.

2 Sketch *six* of your own designs on any theme in which movement from a spring is used. Use markers to colour what you consider are the best two designs, using a different method of shading for each.

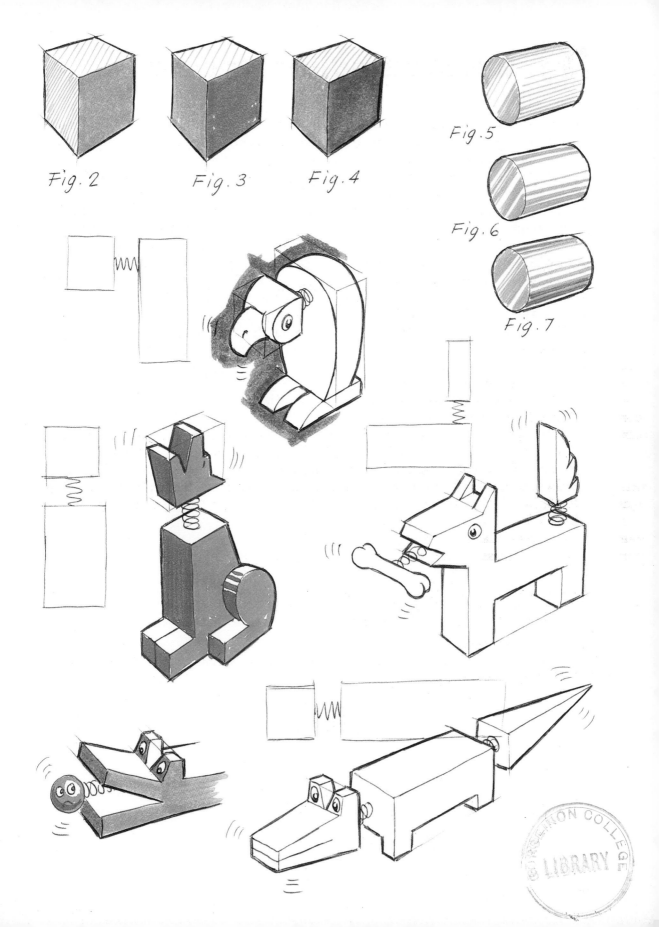

Fig. 2

Fig. 3

Fig. 4

Fig. 5

Fig. 6

Fig. 7

18 Mixing media

Different types of drawing and colouring media can be used on the same page of design sketches or even on a single sketch. It must be borne in mind that too many combinations on one page may produce a disjointed visual effect. If media are combined they should give impact to the sketches and should in no way blur, confuse, or detract from the design.

The sketch in Fig. 1 shows how a wooden figure is moved up and down when a toy vehicle is pushed along. The mechanism has been drawn with a brown marker and shaded with a coloured pencil. The locations of the wooden figure and the mechanism are indicated by the 'ghosted' view of the body of the vehicle. This has been drawn in blue to contrast in colour with the brown and has been left unshaded so that attention is concentrated on the mechanism.

The other sketches opposite are designs for simple wooden candle holders. They demonstrate some of the combinations of media that can be used.

Experiment and find the combinations of media which are best suited to your style and most effective in presenting sketches for design assignments.

Exercise 18

1 Make a series of coloured sketches of designs for a holder for a single candle using as many combinations of media as you can.
The point of this experiment is to find which combinations work, so do not think that you have to start again if some prove unacceptable.

2 Sketch six designs for wooden candle holders that will each hold three candles. Use what you consider to be the most effective combination of media to improve the presentation of your best designs.

Answers to page 23
A Cylindrical tower.
B Cylindrical tower with a conical spire.
C Rectangular block building with a ridged roof.
D Rectangular block building with another block on top.

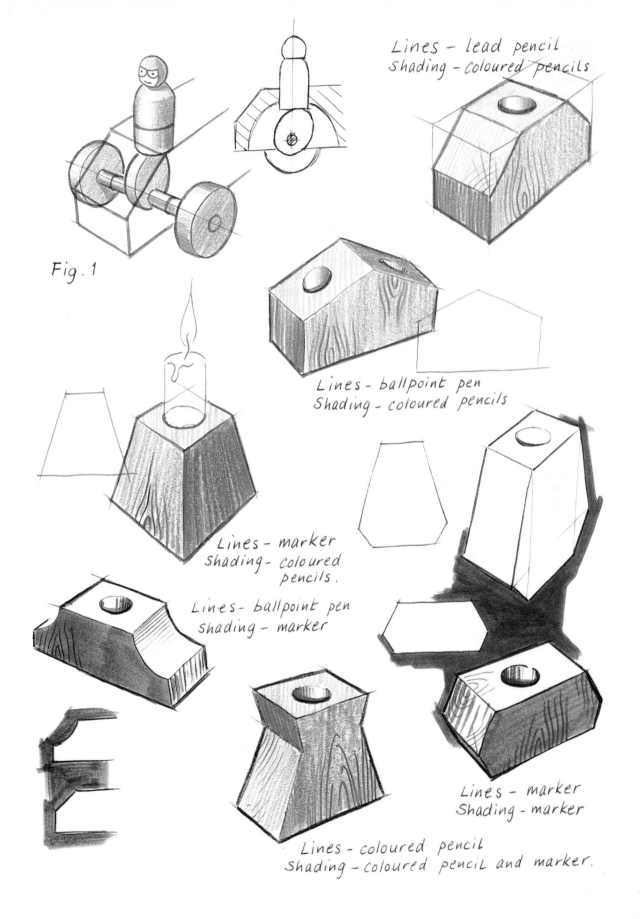

Lines – lead pencil
Shading – Coloured pencils

Fig. 1

Lines – ballpoint pen
Shading – coloured pencils

Lines – marker
Shading – coloured
pencils.

Lines – ballpoint pen
shading – marker

Lines – marker
Shading – marker

Lines – coloured pencil
Shading – coloured pencil and marker.

20 Two-dimensional illustration on coloured paper

Illustrations of flat pieces of jewellery, some of which would be suitable for pendants or for parts of necklaces, are shown in Fig. 1. These illustrations were produced on brushwork paper which can be obtained in a wide range of colours.

The shading techniques which are described below can be used on any type of coloured paper or card, although a wider range of shading effects can be obtained on surfaces which are rough or textured. Ingres or pastel paper, obtainable from art shops, is ideal but expensive.

Choose paper which is a subdued colour such as grey, brown, dull green, or dull blue. This ensures that an illustration is not overpowered by a startling background.

Fig. 2 shows the sequence for producing illustrations like those in Fig. 1. The notes below explain the numbered stages in the sequence:

1 The shape was sketched with a white pencil.
2 It was imagined that light was falling from the top left. The white pencil was used to highlight edges which faced the light.
3 Reflections were added with a white pencil to indicate shiny material.
4 The areas between the reflections were shaded with a coloured pencil or marker to show the colour of the material.
5 A sharp black coloured pencil was used to outline the edges facing away from the light heavily and to outline the edges facing towards the light lightly.
6 Shadows would be cast if the necklace was lying on the paper. The most suitable position for the imaginary light source was chosen and the probable shape of the shadows were then added in a colour which is a darker tone of the colour of the paper.
7 The white edges which would reflect most light were painted with white water-based paint. This stage is not essential but can be used to brighten white highlights. If it is difficult to get a sharp point on a brush, load the brush with paint and draw the hairs against the side wall of the palette until a narrow chisel tip is produced. Alternatively a ruling pen can be used.

Fig. 3 shows two orthographic views of a trinket box, which have been produced using the sequence above.

Exercise 20
1 Draw two of the shapes in Fig. 1 on to coloured paper, slightly larger than the printed size. Colour and line your drawings by following the sequence outline above.

2 Use a white pencil to draw on coloured paper two of your designs for nameplates which you produced for Exercise 14. Use the lining and shading techniques described above to make the illustrations as realistic as possible.

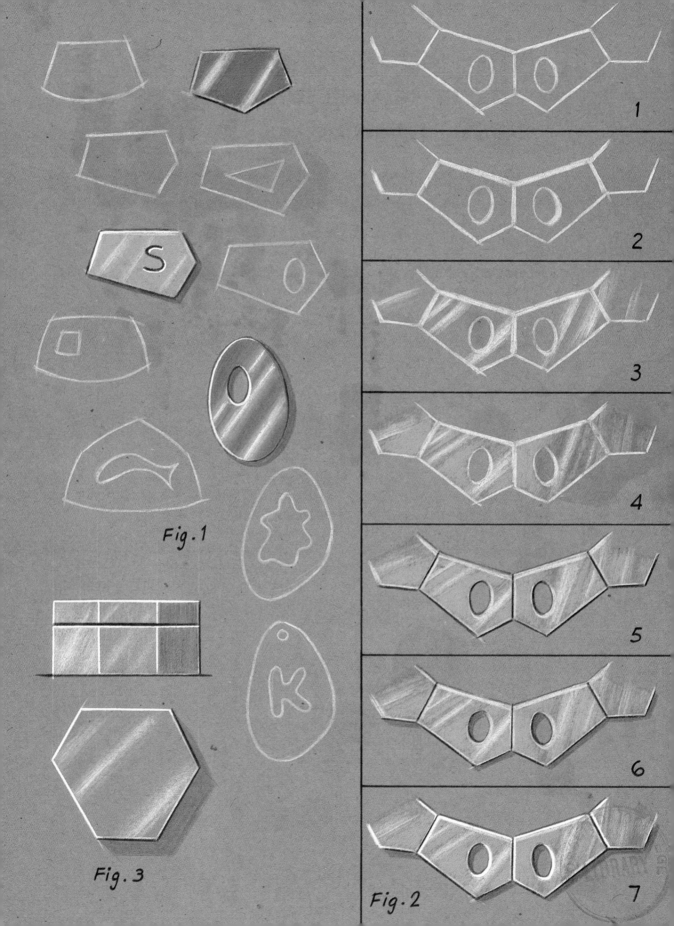

Fig. 1

Fig. 3

Fig. 2

1

2

3

4

5

6

7

22 Water-colour washes

Paint is not often used for design sketches because it takes too long to dry, but it is used in the preparation of more formal illustrations.

Water-colour paints are pigments bound in water-soluble gum. They are available as small cakes of paint or in tubes. When colouring small areas, the paint can be mixed with very little water so that it is quite thick. If a larger area is to be coloured, the paint can be thinned down so that it is transparent enough to allow the lines of the drawing to show through the colour. This is known as **water-colour wash**. (Before applying any paint make sure that the linework will not smudge).

A brown wash was applied to the table lamp in Fig. 1 and then, when this was dry, the shadow was added using another layer of the same colour-wash. This figure also shows how colour-wash can be used to draw attention to accompanying notes.

Painting larger areas requires more careful handling of the paper. As the term 'colour-wash' implies, the paper can become very wet and will probably stretch and buckle. To prevent this, the paper should be pre-stretched before the colour wash is applied. Wet the paper with a damp sponge, and use strips of gummed paper to secure it to a flat wooden board whilst it is still wet (Fig. 2). As the paper dries, it will contract and pull taut against the gummed strips, giving a working surface which, when fully dry, will remain flat when paint is applied. (It does not matter whether you draw before or after the paper is stretched).

To apply a flat colour-wash, mix enough paint to cover the area, tilt the board, and paint on the colour-wash with broad horizontal strokes working quickly from the top to the bottom (Fig. 3). As soon as the area is covered, squeeze the mixture out of the brush with your fingers (Fig. 4), then dip this brush in any excess paint that has accumulated at the lower edge of your painted area. The hairs will absorb the excess paint through capillary action (Fig. 5).

Another method of getting a flat wash is to apply a layer of clean water to the area with a brush. Allow it to dry partially so that the shine has left the surface, and then apply a colour-wash as before. There is less chance of streaks occurring with this method than with the previous one.

Exercise 22

1 Draw the orthographic view of the shelf unit in Fig. 6 on cartridge paper. Apply a colour-wash over this sketch and leave to dry. Then using the same mixture of colour wash, add the shadows.

2 Draw, about twice the printed size, one of the orthographic views of the book ends from page 42 on cartridge paper. Pre-stretch the paper and colour-wash your drawing.

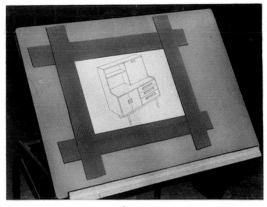

Fig. 2

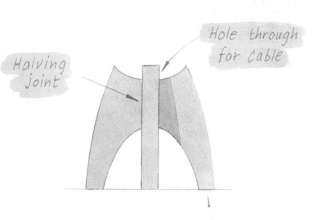

Fig. 1

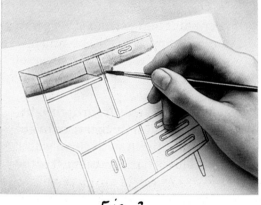

Fig. 3

Fig. 4

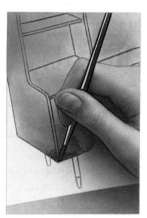

Fig. 5

Streaks in paint, too much time between brush strokes.

Excess colour has not been removed

Shadows added over a flat colour wash.

Fig. 6

23 Water-colour illustration

Variations in tone can be obtained with water-colour in two ways. Either superimpose one layer of wash on another or mix the different tones individually before painting. With either method each application of paint must be left to dry before starting on the next.

Fig. 1 shows the sequence in building up an illustration with layers of the same mixture of water-colour. The stages should be as follows.

1 Colour-wash the whole sketch.
2 Colour-wash all surfaces *except* those which face upwards.
3 Colour-wash all surfaces facing away from the light.
4 Add the shadows with another colour-wash.
5 Wood grain can be added by one of the following methods.
   i) Paint each line of the grain with a fine brush.
or ii) Prepare a brush which has been dipped in thicker paint and 'scrubbed' on scrap paper until the hairs or bristles stand out in small clumps (Fig. 2). The brush should retain enough paint so that when it is drawn over the surface, a series of wavy lines to represent the grain are produced (Fig. 3).

The shading on a curved surface (Fig. 4) changes gradually and evenly from highlight to shadow. With water-colour this effect can be obtained by applying a thicker mixture of paint down the edges and brushing some of this towards the highlight with clean water, thinning the colour in the process. Remember that the highlight is the lightest part of the curved surface and can remain white.

Coloured drawing inks can be used instead of water-colour, the method of application being the same. The transparent inks can be thinned with water, if necessary, to produce paler tints.

Exercise 23
For the following, work on pre-stretched paper.

1 Draw the chessman in Fig. 1 slightly larger than the printed size. Colour-wash your drawing to show the effect of light assuming that the light falls from the right-hand side instead of the left.

2 Produce a colour-washed illustration of the chessman in Fig. 4, slightly larger than the printed size. Assume that light falls from the right-hand side.

3 Copy one of the pictorial views of your model vehicles produced for Exercise 4 and produce a colour-washed illustration.

4 Produce colour-washed illustrations of the birdbox and the frog ornament on page 12 about twice the printed size.

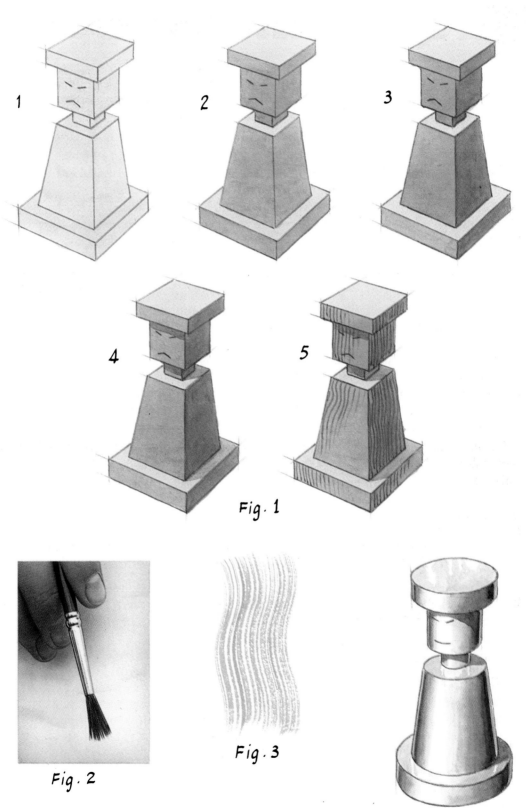

1

2

3

4

5

Fig. 1

Fig. 2

Fig. 3

Fig. 4

24 Opaque water-based paints

The word 'opaque' means non-transparent. An opaque paint is one which covers up another colour completely. Opaque colours create visual impact because they can be bright and rich.

Examples of opaque water-based paints are; water-colour, if mixed with very little water; poster-colour; gouache; designers' colours; fashion colours; acrylic paint. When mixing these paints, water should be used sparingly so that the mixture is thick enough to completely obscure the colour of the paper.

To make a colour lighter or darker, other colours must be added rather than changing the amount of water in the mixture. In the paperweight picture in Fig. 1 the darkest surface was painted with green paint without any other colour added; and the other surfaces were painted with the same green mixed with varying amounts of white paint to lighten the colour. To darken an opaque paint, black or grey can be added, but the resulting colour tends to be lifeless. An alternative method, in which the richness of the colour is retained, is to add a *small* amount of the complementary colour.

The complementary colour can be found in the following way. Fig. 3 shows a colour wheel with the primary colours — red, yellow and blue, and the secondary colours — orange, green and purple. You will see that the secondary colour orange is positioned between the two primary colours which produce it — red and yellow. Similarly green is produced by yellow and blue, and purple by blue and red. Complementary colours are opposite each other on the colour wheel so that, for example, the complementary colour of yellow is purple.

In Fig. 2 the green which was used for the top surface was made darker for the other main surfaces of the paperweight by adding small amounts of red.

Brown and grey do not have complementary colours so they can only be darkened by adding a darker brown, darker grey, or black.

The curved surface of the paperweight in Fig. 4 was first painted with blue and allowed to dry. A white highlight was added and the two colours were blended together with water.

The sequence in Fig. 5 shows the stages in preparing a painted illustration of part of a necklace. This is similar to the sequence on page 40 where coloured pencils were used.

The illustration of the candle holder on the blue background in Fig. 6 is a careful application of the techniques outlined on page 42, carried out in paint.

Exercise 24
1 Draw, on white paper, six designs for paperweights in the same form as those shown in Figs. 1 and 2. Colour them with opaque water-based paints.
2 Repeat question 1 but make your designs in the same form as Fig. 4.
3 Sketch six designs for pendants on coloured paper similar to those shown on page 40. Paint one following the stages shown in Fig. 5 opposite.
4 On coloured paper copy one of your designs for the trinket box drawn in Exercise 7. Paint your drawing using Fig. 6 opposite as a guide.

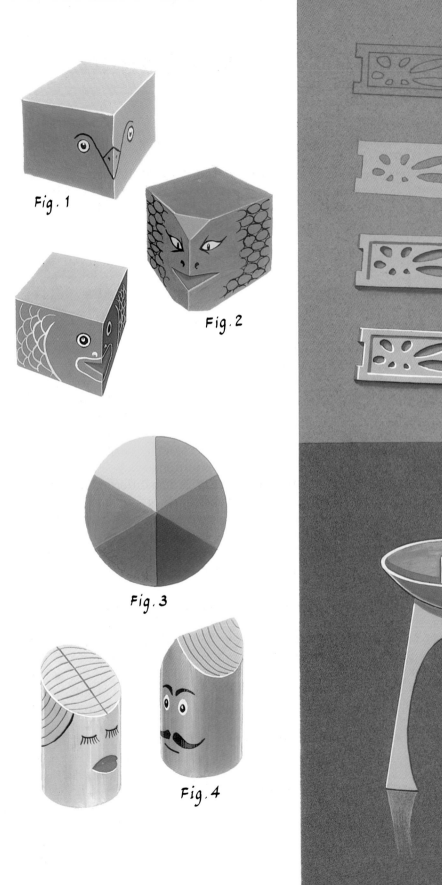

Fig. 1

Fig. 2

Fig. 3

Fig. 4

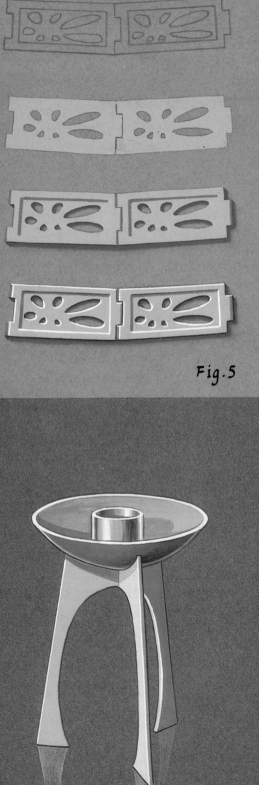

Fig. 5

Fig. 6

25 Paint spatter, chalk and pastel

Toothbrush spatter

A coarse stippled effect can be obtained by spattering paint from a toothbrush. In design work this technique is normally used to provide a vignetted background for a sketch.

Toothbrush spattering is applied as follows. Paint the bristles of a toothbrush with water-based paint (or ink). Then the brush is gently pulled across the edge of a ruler (Fig. 1), so that as the bristles spring back, they release minute droplets of paint which fall onto the paper. The disadvantage of this technique is that a mask must be prepared to cover the drawing, and this takes time.

Fig. 2 shows the vignetted result (of Fig. 1) when the mask, and the weight which held it down, has been removed.

This spatter method can also be used to colour the actual drawing, provided the form is not too complex. The mask shown in Fig. 3 was used for the box in Fig. 4. The surfaces of the box were coloured with different amounts of spattered paint to indicate the effect of light.

Chalk and pastel

In design presentation, chalk and pastel are mainly used for colouring large areas or for reflections. Masks can be used to restrict the colour to the required area.

The mask in Fig. 3 was also used to produce the box in Fig. 5. The different tones were obtained by varying the amounts of colour deposited on each surface from one pastel stick. The reflections below the box were made by smudging the colour down over a straight piece of paper. The reflections on the top of the box were made with white chalk.

The irregular reflection on the side of the car (Fig. 6) was produced by shading with a pastel over the edge of a torn paper mask. A mask cut to the exact shapes was used for the grey lower panels.

Being able to blend colour in this way is useful but unwanted smudges can be caused by careless handling. To prevent smudging, chalk or pastel work must be sealed with a fixative. Fixative can be brushed or sprayed on, either by blowing through a spray diffuser or by using an aerosol can of fixative spray. Some other types of aerosol spray such as hair lacquer or air freshener can also be used satisfactorily.

Any final linework should be added after the illustration has been 'fixed'. Ballpoint pens and markers work well but any loose particles of chalk tend to clog technical pens.

Exercise 25
1 Make a mask and produce a spattered head vignette similar to Fig. 2.
2 Draw a box about twice as big as that shown in Fig. 4. Make it into a mask like that in Fig. 3. Produce a spattered illustration of the box.
3 Use the mask that you made for question 2 to produce an illustration of the box coloured with pastels or chalks.
4 Copy one of the designs for a car body you drew in Exercise 4 and colour it with pastels or chalks.

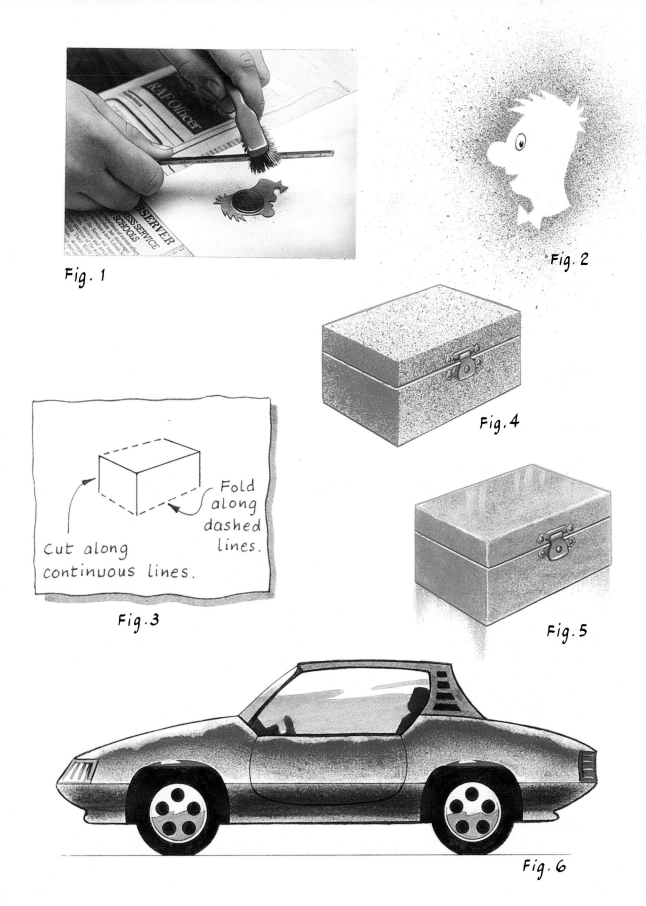

Fig. 1

Fig. 2

Fig. 3

Cut along
continuous lines.

Fold
along
dashed
lines.

Fig. 4

Fig. 5

Fig. 6

26 Airbrushes

An airbrush is a hand-held precision instrument which atomises thinned-down ink or paint into a fine spray for use in graphic work.

Fig. 1 shows an airbrush connected through a hose and a pressure control valve to its air supply which, in this case, is a can of airbrush propellant. Alternatively, the air could be supled from a compressor or even from a car tyre fitted with a suitable adaptor. Generally the pressure should be 25–30 lbs/in².

An airbrush for graphic work should be capable of spraying fine lines. In fact, you should be able to 'write' almost normally with it (Fig. 2). It is not possible to do this with the cheapest airbrushes which are made primarily for modelmakers so these should be avoided.

There are two basic types of airbrush:

I Single-action airbrushes

(An example is shown in Fig. 1). The name refers to the single action of the control button which, when pressed, produces the spray. The jet, or in some cases the needle, is adjusted before spraying to control the amount of mixture being sprayed. This type of airbrush is particularly suitable for beginners because the amount of mixture sprayed will remain constant once the adjustment has been made.

2 Double-action airbrushes

(An example is shown in Fig. 3). This type has a double-action control lever: pressing down releases air and pulling back withdraws the needle to allow paint to flow to the jet. The further back that the lever is pulled the more dense the spray.

Some practice is necessary before the sensitive movement of the lever can be controlled well enough to produce good results. Some double-action airbrushes can be converted to single action, giving a consistent spray density, by moving an adjustable cam ring or a screw.

There are variations in the design of airbrushes; the most noticeable is the type of reservoir. For example, although the single-action airbrush shown in Fig. 1 has a removable jar, this type of instrument from another manufacturer might have a reservoir like that shown in Fig. 3. Alternatively, a single- or double-action airbrush might have a small cup which fits into the side of the instrument and which can be easily removed to change the colour.

Careful and efficient cleaning of an airbrush is essential. The reservoir must be cleaned thoroughly, and clean water sprayed out to wash away any paint/ink clinging to the jet and needle. From time to time more specialised cleaning and servicing are necessary in accordance with manufacturers' instructions.

Most thinned-down water-based paints and inks are safe to use in an airbrush provided they are free from coarse particles. Concentrated water colours and inks can be obtained which are specially made for use with an airbrush.

Pressure
Control
valve

Air supply

Air control
button

Adjustable
jet

Reservoir

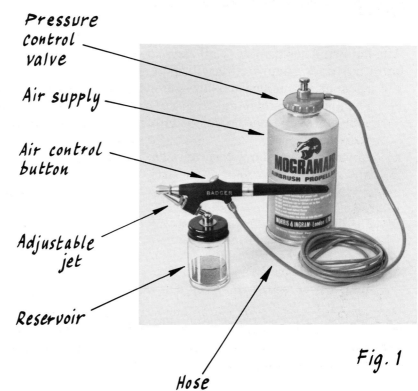

Hose

Fig. 1

James

Fig. 2

Reservoir   Control lever

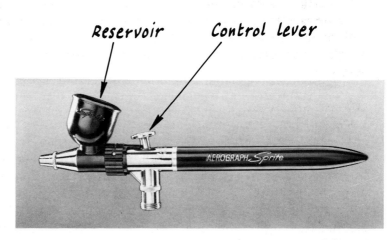

Fig. 3

27 Airbrushing exercises

The following notes apply to all exercises:
a) Use a dark colour — this will show any mistakes or poor technique very clearly.
b) The masks required are shown alongside each figure.
c) The masks should be cut from cartridge paper with scissors or a sharp blade. Make your masks so that the finished illustrations will be about twice the printed size shown.
d) Always start and finish spraying on the masks wherever possible. You will in this way avoid excess colour on the artwork.

Exercises (Exercise 1 corresponds to Fig. 1 and so on)
1 Mix some ink or water-colour with water. Load the reservoir of the airbrush and spray bands and lines. For broad bands and uniform tones keep the airbrush about 100 mm from the paper. Move the airbrush closer to the paper for narrower bands until a fine line is obtained (with a single-action airbrush, the jet must be adjusted to give a fine line). If the sprayed areas appear mottled, the mixture is too weak and more ink or paint should be added.
   Try to write your name.
2 Spray along the straight edge of a piece of paper to give a tone with a neat edge which fades into a vignette.
3 A simple landscape can be produced as follows. Spray over a straight piece of paper and fade away as in Fig. 2. Draw and cut out a simple negative mask of a landscape and spray to give a silhouetted effect. Turn the mask over and upside down. Spray lightly to give the reflection of the landscape as if in water. Place a coin in position and spray round it for the moon and repeat with a light spray for the reflection. Add one or two light freehand streaks with the airbrush to form clouds (with experience birds can be added in the sky as well).
4 Cut out a mask of your initials. Lightly spray all over and then spray bands of different widths diagonally across, to give the effect of reflections.
5 Cut a mask with a circular hole and spray a sphere.
6 Cut a mask with a rectangular hole and use it in two positions to spray the orthographic view of a cylindrical pin.
7 Use the same rectangular mask to spray a rectangle which has the same even tone all over.
8 Cut out a mask similar to that shown in Fig. 3 on page 50 and spray a cube. Build up the tones of the surfaces with a number of sprayed layers of colour.
9 Using straight pieces of loose paper and your cube mask, add the shadow and reflections to your sprayed cube.
10 Draw and cut out a mask for each of the solids shown. Spray to reproduce the given shading.
11 Draw a combination of solids to form a simple building, like the one shown. Work out your own masking sequence and produce an airbrushed illustration.

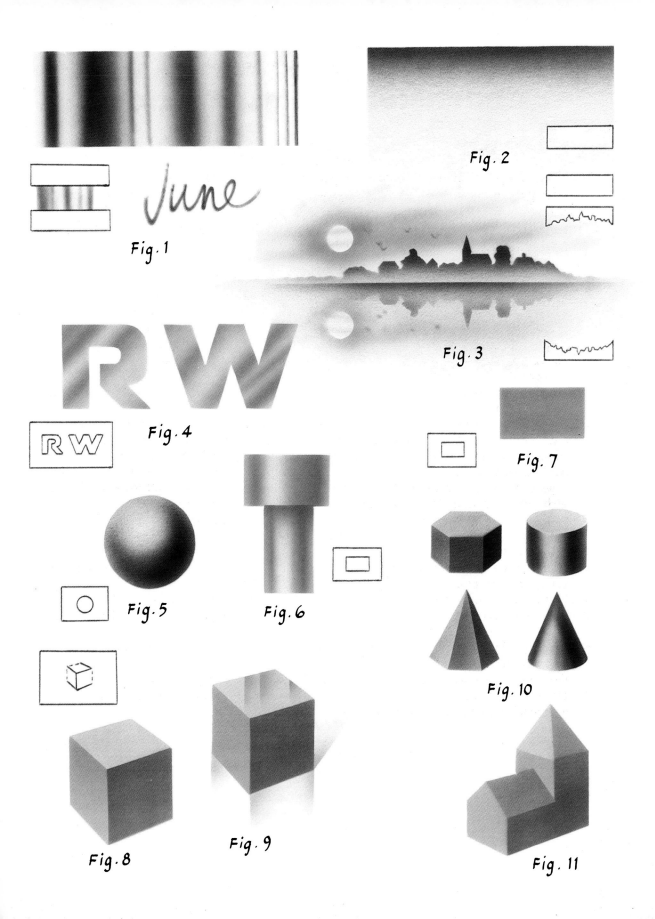

June

Fig. 1

Fig. 2

Fig. 3

Fig. 4

Fig. 5

Fig. 6

Fig. 7

Fig. 8

Fig. 9

Fig. 10

Fig. 11

28 Examples of three-dimensional presentation

The hairdryer and the trinket box opposite are each shown presented in three different ways using the techniques described in the previous chapters.

The illustrations were produced using the following:

Fig. 1   **Coloured pencils and black ballpoint pen**
Note the use of reflected light to emphasise the curved surfaces in each of the illustrations of the hairdryer.

Fig. 2   **Markers**
Bar shading is usually used to show the form of curved surfaces when using markers.

Fig. 3   **Airbrushed with ink and concentrated water colour**
Gouache was used for the linework.
   The masks used for this figure and for Fig. 6 were cut from low-tack adhesive clear film. The film is laid over the drawing, and the surface to be sprayed is revealed by cutting a hole in the film to the required shape with a sharp blade. The piece of film which is removed can be replaced in position after spraying and after cutting out the next shape to be sprayed. The low-tack adhesive will not pull paint or ink from a sprayed surface.

Fig. 4   **Black and white pencils and black ballpoint pen**

Fig. 5   **Markers, white coloured pencil, and white gouache**

Fig. 6   **White and black gouache for both airbrushing and linework**
The lines of the letters engraved on the top of the box can be highlighted successfully by imagining they are much larger. Think of the lines as trenches dug into the metal. Fig. 7 for instance, represents part of the letter 'E'. The highlights will occur where both surfaces can be seen meeting at an edge, as outlined in the sequence on page 41.

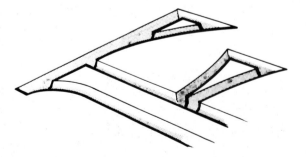

Fig. 7

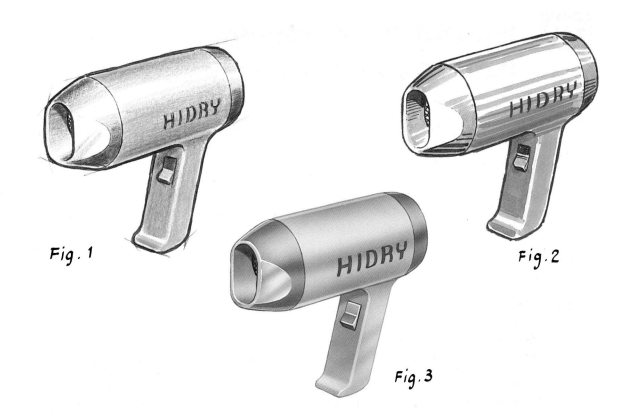

Fig. 1

Fig. 2

Fig. 3

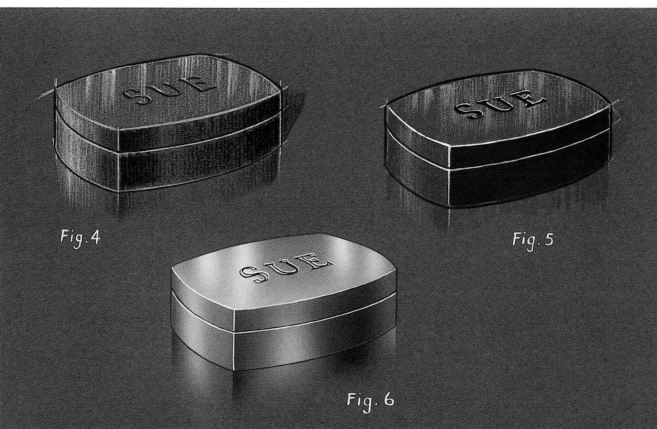

Fig. 4

Fig. 5

Fig. 6

Some suitable materials and equipment

Coloured pencils
Derwent coloured pencils: Cumberland Pencil Company, Keswick
Caran d'Ache water soluble pencils: Switzerland

Pens
'Bic' ballpoint pens
William Mitchell's lettering nibs
Osmiroid fountain pens with interchangeable nibs

Markers
'Colourpen' for linework
'Brushline' for colouring
'Notewriter' for notetaking
All these from Berol Ltd, King's Lynn

Water colours and designers gouache
George Rowney & Company Ltd, Bracknell
Winsor & Newton Ltd, Wealdstone

Transparent drawing inks
Winsor & Newton Ltd, Wealdstone

Lettering stencils
UNO pen stencils
Standardgraph stencils

Dry-transfer lettering
Letraset UK Ltd, London

Airbrushes
'Badger' airbrushes — sole agents: Morris & Ingram (London) Ltd, Poole
'Aerograph' airbrushes: The DeVilbiss Company Ltd, Bournemouth

Colouring media suitable for spraying
'Magic Color': Royal Sovereign Graphics, London
'Dr Martin's Radiant Concentrated Water Color': Salis International, Florida, USA

Airbrush propellant
'Speedry Magic Marker Airbrush Propellant: Royal Sovereign Graphics, London
'Mogramair Airbrush Propellant': Morris & Ingram (London) Ltd, Poole

Low-tack Masking Film
'Speedry Magic Marker Masking Film': Royal Sovereign Graphics, London